GRAPHIC EXPEDITIONS

SEARCHING FOR UFOs

An Isabel Soto INVESTIGATION

Aaron Sautter

Consultant:
Jerome Clark, Editor
International UFO Reporter
J. Allen Hynek Center for UFO Studies
Chicago, Illinois, USA

illustrated by Cynthia Martin and Barbara Schulz

www.raintreepublishers.co.uk
Visit our website to find out
more information about
Raintree books.

To order:
☎ Phone 0845 6044371
📄 Fax +44 (0) 1865 312263
✉ Email myorders@raintreepublishers.co.uk

Customers from outside the UK please telephone +44 1865 312262

Raintree is an imprint of Capstone Global Library Limited, a company incorporated in England and
Wales having its registered office at 7 Pilgrim Street, London EC4V 6LB
Registered company number: 6695882

British Library Cataloguing in Publication Data
Sautter, Aaron – Searching for UFOs: an Isabel Soto investigation
A full catalogue record for this book is available from the British Library.

ISBN 978 1 406 21814 5 (hardback)
14 13 12 11 10
10 9 8 7 6 5 4 3 2 1

Designer: Alison Thiele
Cover Artist: Tod Smith
Colourist: Krista Ward
Media reseracher: Wanda Winch
UK Editor: Diyan Leake
Originated by Capstone Global Library Ltd
Printed and bound in China by South China Printing Company Limited

Photo Credits: CORBIS/Bettmann, 25; Fortean Picture Library, 15; iStockphoto/Joze
Pojbic, 19

Design Elements: Shutterstock/Chen Ping Hung (framed edge design); mmmm (world
map design); Mushakesa (abstract lines design); Najin (old parchment design)

CONTENTS

Strange lights and objects in the sky have been reported for thousands of years.

In Egypt, a few ancient hieroglyphs look like modern aircraft. Some people think the symbols really show different types of UFOs.

Thousands of years ago, people in the Nazca Desert in Peru dug lines into the ground. They drew huge animals, people, and geometric symbols.

The Nazca Lines are so big that they can only be seen from the air. Some people believe the lines were signposts and landing strips for visiting UFOs.

In 1561, dozens of UFOs were reported over Nuremberg, Germany.

A painting of the event shows many cylinder-shaped objects and colourful spheres. They seem to fight a battle in the sky.

I took the debris to Carswell Air Force Base.

General Roger Ramey said the newspaper reports of a UFO crash weren't true. He had a reporter take a photo of me with some of the debris.

ROSWELL DAILY

Gen. Ramey Empties Roswell Saucer

The next day, a press release said that the material was really from a crashed weather balloon.

The material I found didn't look like a weather balloon to me. I think the material was switched before they took my photo.

I'm certain the real debris didn't come from earth.

Did the material look anything like this?

Hard to say. The pieces were broken apart.

Thanks for your time, Major Marcel. I think we need to look at some other kinds of UFOs.

THE FIRST FLYING SAUCERS

On 24 June 1947, Kenneth Arnold was flying his small plane near Mount Rainier in Washington State. Suddenly he saw nine strange objects flying at fantastic speeds. Arnold said the objects flew "like a saucer would if you skip it across water". Newspapers started calling the objects "flying saucers". The term stuck.

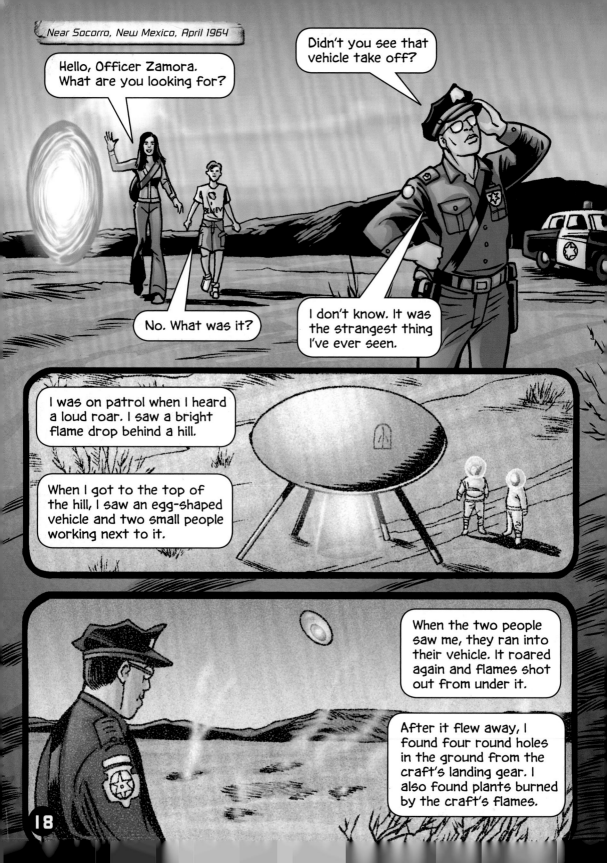

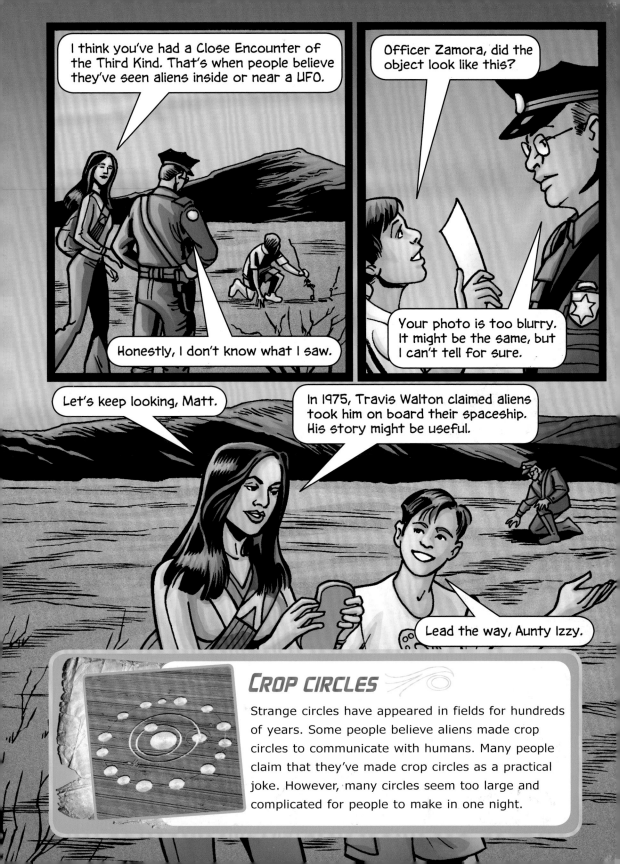

CROP CIRCLES

Strange circles have appeared in fields for hundreds of years. Some people believe aliens made crop circles to communicate with humans. Many people claim that they've made crop circles as a practical joke. However, many circles seem too large and complicated for people to make in one night.

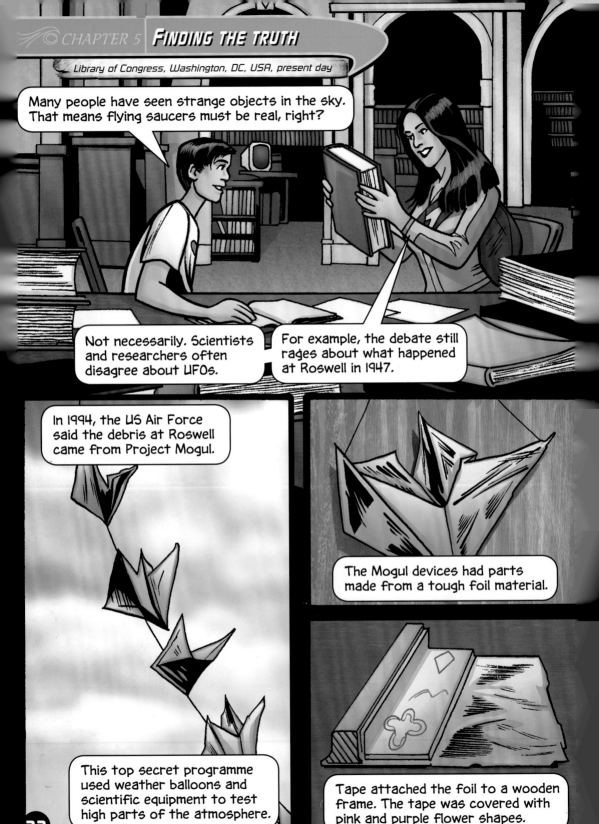

Library of Congress, Washington, DC, USA, present day

Many people have seen strange objects in the sky. That means flying saucers must be real, right?

Not necessarily. Scientists and researchers often disagree about UFOs.

For example, the debate still rages about what happened at Roswell in 1947.

In 1994, the US Air Force said the debris at Roswell came from Project Mogul.

The Mogul devices had parts made from a tough foil material.

This top secret programme used weather balloons and scientific equipment to test high parts of the atmosphere.

Tape attached the foil to a wooden frame. The tape was covered with pink and purple flower shapes.

But some UFO researchers think the Air Force report is flawed. They believe the wind would have blown a Mogul device far away from Brazel's ranch.

They also say that the Mogul devices were too small to explain the amount of debris found.

I'm confused. Was the debris from a spacecraft or not?

Nobody knows. The debris seems too flimsy for a spacecraft. But the Air Force report overlooks important details.

Something crashed near Roswell in 1947, but the mystery may never be explained.

ALIEN AUTOPSY HOAX

In the 1990s, filmmaker Ray Santilli claimed he had film footage of a dead alien from Roswell. In the film, doctors performed an autopsy on an alien body. The film was very popular. But in 2006, Santilli admitted the film was fake. The alien was a dummy with animal organs placed inside to look like alien body parts.

Another problem with UFO reports is that people often mistake ordinary things for UFOs.

Lenticular clouds look flat and round. They're often mistaken for flying saucers.

Secret military aircraft have been around for many years. People might easily mistake these strange aeroplanes for black triangle UFOs.

Meteors burning up in the Earth's atmosphere are often mistaken for alien spacecraft.

People have mistaken Venus and the Moon for UFOs, too.

Near the northern and southern poles, auroras glow in the night sky. From a distance, they could look like lights from UFOs.

Some scientists believe ball lightning can explain a few UFO sightings. These rare balls of energy can hover in place or even explode like a bomb.

I think your UFO may have a natural explanation. Did you notice anything else about it?

It was pretty far away, but I heard a boom before it disappeared.

Hmm. You probably saw a meteor or ball lightning. They aren't UFOs, but you're lucky to have seen one up close.

I think it's time we got back to your mum.

PROJECT BLUE BOOK

From 1952 to 1970, Project Blue Book investigated thousands of UFO sightings for the US Air Force. This team of scientists wanted to find out if UFOs were real. They determined that most UFOs were either hoaxes or had logical explanations. However, a small number of UFO reports were unexplainable.

Hi, Mum.

Did you solve the mystery of your UFO?

I think Matt saw some ball lightning or a meteor. He's lucky he got a photo of it.

After everybody we talked to, I was sure I saw a real UFO.

BELIEVE

ROSWELL UFO FESTIVAL

Don't be disappointed. We may not know for sure if UFOs have visited Earth . . .

. . . but the universe is huge. Maybe aliens are out there, just waiting to meet us.

HARRY'S ANTIQUES

MORE ABOUT

UFOs

Several people claim Men in Black, or MIBs, visited them after UFO sightings. These men dress in black suits, black hats, and dark sunglasses. They claim to work for the government and usually threaten UFO witnesses if they talk about what they saw. Nobody knows if these mysterious men are real or not.

In 1938, Orson Welles broadcast a radio play of *The War of the Worlds*. It was presented as a news bulletin announcing that Martians were invading New York. The broadcast caused people to panic because they believed aliens had actually landed. The next day Welles and the radio station had to explain that the news announcement was part of the play.

People have claimed to see many kinds of aliens. The Greys are one of the most common. These short, hairless aliens have grey skin, large black eyes, and a small slit for a mouth. Nordic aliens look like humans. They are tall, muscular, and have blonde hair and large blue or yellow eyes. Some alien sightings include small green, goblin-like creatures with bulging yellow eyes. Others have thick, wrinkly skin like an elephant.

The US Air Force develops and tests secret experimental aircraft at Area 51 in Nevada. UFO sightings and other strange things are often reported near Area 51. Many people believe the US government experiments with captured UFOs there.

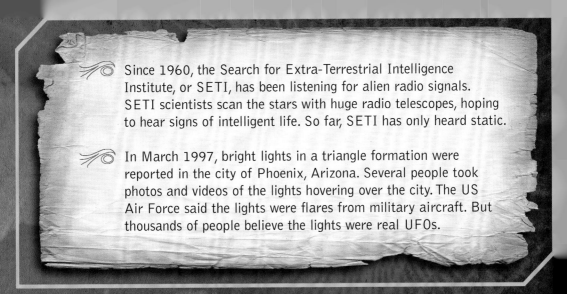

Since 1960, the Search for Extra-Terrestrial Intelligence Institute, or SETI, has been listening for alien radio signals. SETI scientists scan the stars with huge radio telescopes, hoping to hear signs of intelligent life. So far, SETI has only heard static.

In March 1997, bright lights in a triangle formation were reported in the city of Phoenix, Arizona. Several people took photos and videos of the lights hovering over the city. The US Air Force said the lights were flares from military aircraft. But thousands of people believe the lights were real UFOs.

MORE ABOUT

Isabel Soto

NAME: Isabel "Izzy" Soto
INTERESTS: People and places
BUILD: Athletic   *HAIR:* Dark Brown
EYES: Brown   *HEIGHT:* 1.70 m

WISP: The Worldwide Inter-dimensional Space/Time Portal developed by Max Axiom at Axiom Laboratory.

BACKSTORY: Isabel "Izzy" Soto caught the humanities bug as a little girl. Every night, her grandfather told her about his adventures exploring ancient ruins in South America. He believed people can learn a lot from other cultures and places.

Izzy's interest in cultures followed her through school and beyond. She studied history and geography. On one research trip, she discovered an ancient stone with mysterious energy. Izzy took the stone to Super Scientist Max Axiom, who determined that the stone's energy cuts across space and time. Harnessing the power of the stone, he built a device called the WISP. It opens windows to any place and any time. Although she must not use the WISP to change history, Izzy now explores events wherever and whenever they happen, solving a few mysteries along the way.

GLOSSARY

abduct take someone away by force

atomic bomb bomb that splits atoms and explodes with great force. Atomic bombs destroy large areas and leave behind dangerous radiation.

aurora colourful bands of light which people can see in the sky if they are far north or far south of the Equator

autopsy detailed study of a dead body to determine the cause and manner of death

close encounter event where someone sees an unidentified flying object

debris scattered pieces of something that has been broken or destroyed

hieroglyph picture or symbol used in the ancient Egyptian system of writing

hoax trick to make people believe something that is not true

incident something that happens; an event

lenticular cloud lens-shaped cloud that is formed at high altitude

meteor piece of rock or dust that enters the Earth's atmosphere, causing a streak of light in the sky

UFO short for *unidentified flying object*: object in the sky thought to be a spaceship from another planet

weather balloon balloon that carries instruments into the air to measure pressure, temperature, and other details about the atmosphere

FIND OUT MORE

BOOKS

Alien Neighbours?: The Solar System, Angela Royston (Raintree, 2006)

The Mystery of Crop Circles (Can Science Solve? series), Chris Oxlade (Heinemann Library, 2006)

The Mystery of UFOs (Can Science Solve? series), Chris Oxlade (Heinemann Library, 2006)

Searching for Life in Space (The Science of... series), Clint Twist (TickTock, 2006)

UFOs: Alien Abductions and Close Encounters (Graphic Mysteries series), Gary Jeffrey (Book House, 2006)

WEBSITES

www.roswellufomuseum.com/Tour/ ~1st-index.html
Take a virtual tour of the UFO Museum and Research Center in Roswell, New Mexico, USA.

www.worldalmanacforkids.com
Go to the "Science" chapter of this website and click on "Space Facts & History," then on "Searching for Life," to find out how the US National Aeronautics and Space Administration searches for signs of life on Mars.

www.esa.int/esaKIDSen
Click on the "Life in Space" tab, then go to the "Are we alone?" menu for facts, audio clips, games, and animations about life beyond Earth.

INDEX